Foreword

The pieces have been chosen to provide the maximum variety of period and style and to give the student a clear idea of the versatility of technique required by the orchestral player.

Keith Puddy

Copyright Acknowledgements

Extract from Symphony No. 1 by Sibelius (page 20) included by kind permission of Breitkopf and Hartel (London) Ltd.

Extract from Seasons by Glazunov (page 21) included by kind permission of Musikverlags M. P. Belaieff, Frankfurt

Extract from Ma Mère l'Oye by Ravel (page 22) included by kind permission of Durand et Cie, Paris

Extract from Pini di Roma by Resphigi (page 23) included by kind permission of G. Ricordi & Co.

Extract from Fifine at the Fair by Bantock (page 25) reprinted by kind permission of Novello & Co. Ltd.

Extracts from Miraculous Mandarin by Bartok (page 26) included by kind permission of Universal Edition (London) Ltd.

Extract from The Young Person's Guide to the Orchestra by Britten (page 28) included by kind permission of the Copyright Owners, Boosey & Hawkes Music Publishers Ltd., Aldwych House, 71-91 Aldwych, London WC2B 4HN

Extracts from Symphony No. 5 by Nielsen (page 29) included by kind permission of Skandinavisk Musikforlag, Copenhagen K

Contents

	No.		Page
MOZART 1756–1791	1	Symphony No. 39 in E flat major	2
BEETHOVEN 1770–1827	2	Piano Concerto No. 1 in C major, Op. 15	2
	3	Pastoral Symphony No. 6 in F, Op. 68	4
ROSSINI 1792–1868	4	Overture "La Cenerentola"	6
	5	Overture "Semiramide"	7
SCHUBERT 1792–1828	6	Symphony No. 8 in B minor (The Unfinished)	7
BERLIOZ 1803–1869	7	The Trojans	8
GLINKA 1803–1857	8	Komarinskaja	8
MENDELSSOHN 1809–1847	9	Fingals Cave Overture	9
VERDI 1813–1901	10	Overture "La forza del destino"	10
WAGNER 1813–1883	11	Overture "Tannhäuser"	10
OFFENBACH 1819–1880	12	Les Contes d'Hoffmann	11
BRAHMS 1833–1897	13	Symphony No. 3 in F major, Op. 90	12
SAINT-SAENS 1835–1921	14	Le Carnaval des Animaux (No. 12 Fossiles)	15
DELIBES 1836–1891	15	Coppélia	15
BORODIN 1833–1887	16	Prince Igor	16
TSCHAIKOWSKY 1840–1893	17	Sleeping Beauty	17
DVORAK 1841–1904	18	Symphony No. 9 (From the New World)	18
RIMSKY-KORSAKOV 1844–1908	19	Capriccio Espagnol, Op. 34	18
SIBELIUS 1868–1957	20	Symphony No. 1	20
GLAZUNOV 1865–1936	21	Seasons	21
DEBUSSY 1862–1918	22	Prelude (A l'après-midi d'un faune)	22
RAVEL 1875–1937	23	Ma mère L'oye	22
RESPIGHI 1879–1936	24	Pini di Roma	23
PROKOFIEFF 1891–1953	25	Peter and the Wolf	23
BANTOCK 1868–1946	26	Fifine at the Fair	25
BARTOK 1881–1945	27	The Miraculous Mandarin	26
BRITTEN 1913	28	The Young Person's Guide to the Orchestra	28
NIELSEN 1865–1931	29	Symphony No. 5	29

Symphony No. 39 in E♭ major

(Trio Menuetto)

B♭ Clarinet

MOZART

Piano Concerto No. 1 in C major, Op. 15

(2nd Movement)

B♭ Clarinet

BEETHOVEN

Clarinet Music

Pastoral Symphony No. 6 in F, Op. 68

Bb Clarinet

BEETHOVEN

Clarinet Music

(2nd Movement)

Andante molto mosso ($\downarrow\cdot$ = 50)

(3rd Movement Scherzo)

B♭ Clarinet

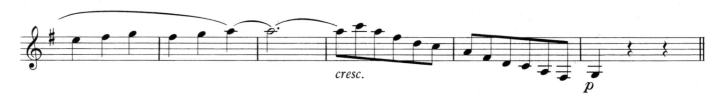

(5th Movement)

Overture "La Cenerentola"

B♭ Clarinet

ROSSINI

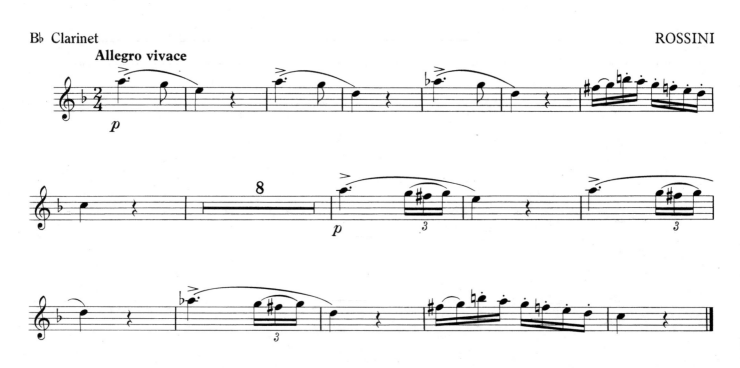

Overture "Semiramide"

A Clarinet

ROSSINI

Symphony No. 8 in B minor (The Unfinished)

A Clarinet

SCHUBERT

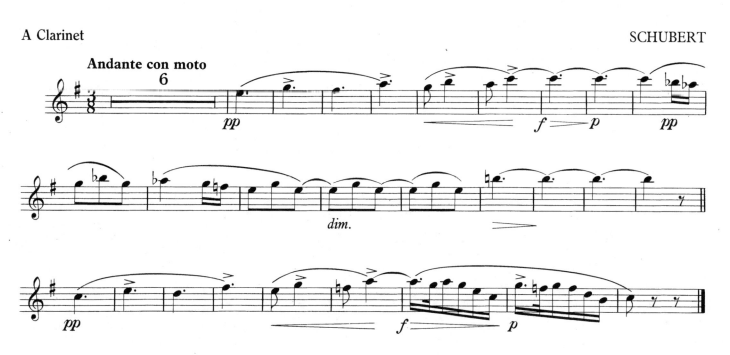

Clarinet Music

The Trojans

(Part I, Act 2, Scene 2)

A Clarinet

BERLIOZ

Komarinskaja

B♭ Clarinet

GLINKA

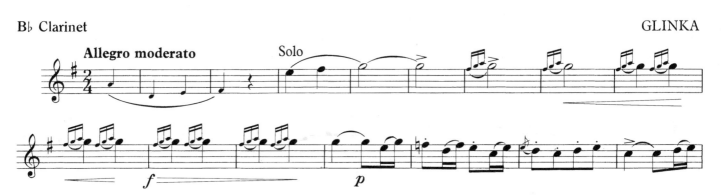

Clarinet Music

Fingals Cave Overture

A Clarinet

MENDELSSOHN

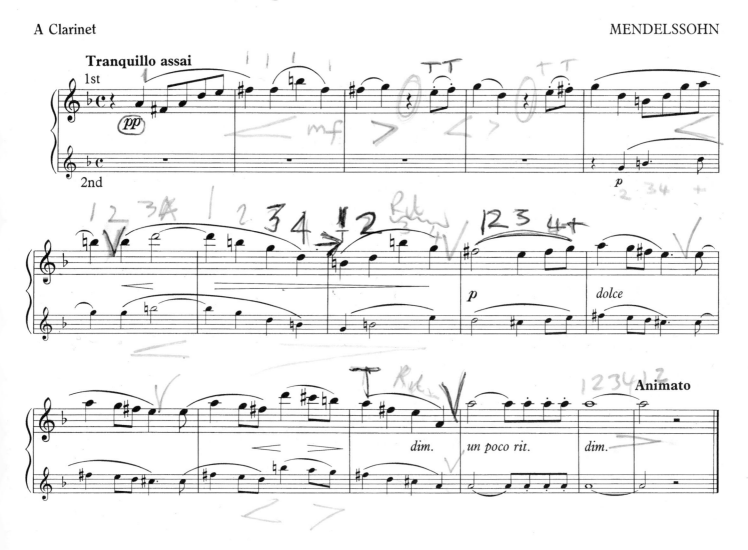

Overture "La forza del destino"

A Clarinet

VERDI

Overture "Tannhäuser"

A Clarinet

WAGNER

Clarinet Music

Les Contes d'Hoffmann

A Clarinet

OFFENBACH

Symphony No. 3 in F major, Op. 90

(1st Movement)

Bb Clarinet

BRAHMS

A Clarinet

sotto voce

p grazioso

change to B♭ clarinet

B♭ Clarinet

Clarinet Music

(2nd Movement)

Bb Clarinet

BRAHMS

Le Carnaval des Animaux

(No. 12 Fossiles)

B♭ Clarinet

SAINT-SAËNS

Coppélia

(4th Variation)

A Clarinet

DELIBES

Prince Igor

B♭ Clarinet

BORODIN

Sleeping Beauty

(Pas de Six)

B♭ Clarinet

TSCHAIKOWSKY

Sleeping Beauty

(No. 25 Blue bird)

A Clarinet

TSCHAIKOWSKY

Symphony No. 9 (From the New World)

(4th Movement)

A Clarinet

DVORAK

Allegro con fuoco ($\text{\textonehalf} = 152$)

Capriccio Espagnol, Op. 34

(3rd Movement Alborada)

B♭ Clarinet

RIMSKY-KORSAKOV

Vivo e strepitoso

(5th Movement Fandango Asturiano)

A Clarinet

RIMSKY-KORSAKOFF

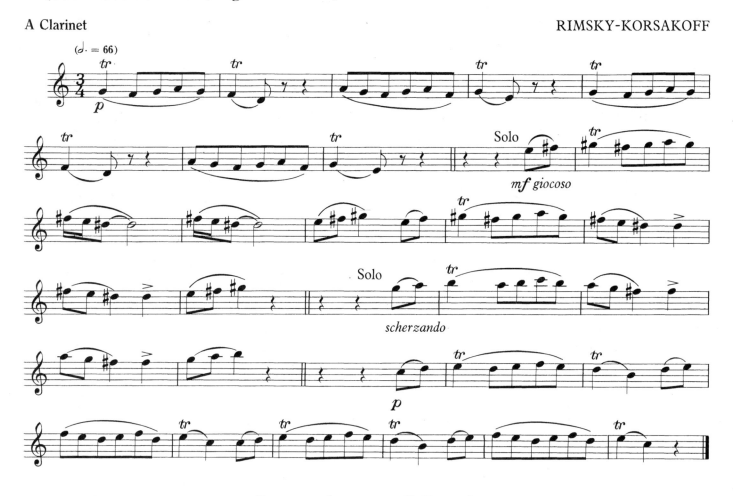

Symphony No. 1

(1st Movement)

A Clarinet

SIBELIUS

Seasons

B♭ Clarinet

GLAZOUNOW

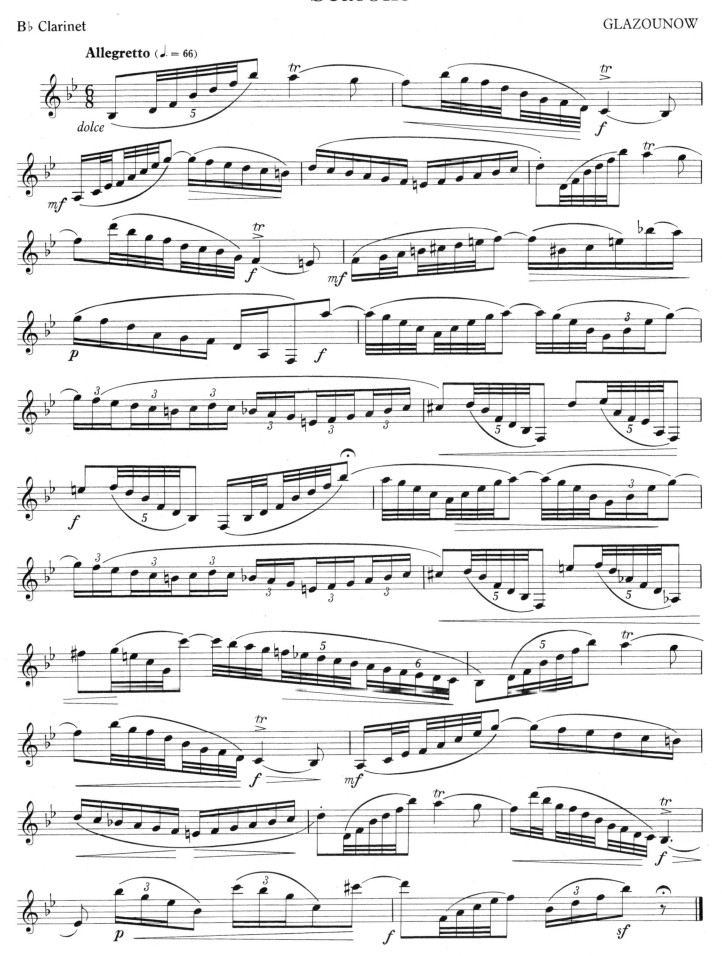

Clarinet Music

Prelude (A l'après-midi d'un faune)

A Clarinet

DEBUSSY

Très modéré

Bb Clarinet **Ier Mouvt.**

Ma mère L'oye

(4th Movement Les entrehens de la Belle et de la Bête)

Bb Clarinet

RAVEL

Mouv't de Valse modéré (♩. = 50)

Clarinet Music

Pini di Roma
(3rd Movement I pini del Gianicolo)

A Clarinet

RESPIGHI

Lento (♩ = 50)

come in sogno *p*

pp

Un poco animato

rall.

6

cresc.

dim.

tempo 1

Peter and the Wolf

A Clarinet

PROKOFIEFF

Moderato

p

con eleganza

2

f

f

2

mf

mf

Fifine at the Fair

Bb Clarinet

BANTOCK

The Miraculous Mandarin

1st decoy game
A Clarinet

BARTÓK

The young person's guide to the orchestra

(Variation C)

B♭ Clarinet

BRITTEN

Symphony No. 5

B♭ Clarinet

NIELSEN

Clarinet Music

Processed and printed by
Halstan & Co. Ltd., Amersham, Bucks., England

CLARINET

ORCHESTRAL EXTRACTS

Selected and edited by Keith Puddy

Containing extracts from pieces by

Mozart Beethoven Rossini Schubert

Berlioz Glinka Mendelssohn Verdi

Wagner Offenbach Brahms Saint-Saëns

Delibes Borodin Tchaikovsky Dvořák

Rimsky-Korsakov Sibelius Glazunov

Debussy Ravel Respighi Prokofiev

Bantock Bartók Britten Nielsen

TCL 002266
ISBN 978-0-8573

COLLEGE LONDON

Published by Trinity College London

© Copyright by Trinity College London

9 780857 36